Essential Skills for Reading Success:

Strategies for Reading Comprehension and Test Taking
Revised

by Howard I. Berrent, Ph.D.
and Edward R. Nasello

RALLY! EDUCATION, LLC

Glen Head, New York

RALLY!
EDUCATION

e all about student success!

ISBN 1-58380-991-0

Printed in the U.S.A.
506.3E

Cover Designer: Jean-Paul Vest
Book Designer: Lori Harley
Editor: Pat Keiserman

RALLY! EDUCATION
22 Railroad Avenue
Glen Head, NY 11545
tel 888·99·RALLY
fax 516·671·7900
www.RALLYEDUCATION.com

Essential Skills for Reading Success
Strategies for Reading Comprehension and Test Taking

Table of Contents

Introduction

Welcome to *Essential Skills for Reading Success: Strategies for Reading Comprehension and Test Taking.* Being a successful reader means that you understand what you read. There are fourteen important skills you need to be a great reader. This book teaches you strategies, which are ways to use the skills when you read. It also teaches you how to answer reading comprehension questions on tests.

Essential Skills for Reading Success has different kinds of reading selections and different types of questions. You will read passages that are poems, and other passages that give you information, tell a story, or explain how to do something. You will be asked multiple-choice questions and questions that require you to write out an answer. When you finish this book you will be a better reader and a better test taker.

Essential Skills for Reading Success is made up of two parts:

Part A will teach you the essential reading comprehension skills one-by-one.

Part B will teach you the essential reading comprehension skills all together.

Throughout the book, we will provide *Strategies, Hints,* and *Reminders* to make learning easier for you. First we will model what we teach. Then we will guide you. Finally we will provide you with independent study to try on your own what you have learned.

When you finish *Essential Skills for Reading Success* you will be a better reader and a better test taker.

PART A

The 14 Essential Skills for Reading Success

One-by-One

Each of the fourteen reading comprehension skills are taught one-by-one in this part. First you will read a passage. You will then be asked some questions.

In **Modeled Instruction,** we will teach you a strategy that you can use to answer each question. Then we will explain each of the answer choices. We will show you why some of the choices are not correct. We will explain why the correct choice is the answer.

In **Guided Instruction,** we will provide *Hints* for you on how to answer the question. The first question will be multiple-choice. The second question will ask you to write out the answer.

In **Independent Study,** you will be on your own. You will answer multiple-choice and open-ended questions.

Skill 1: Facts and Details

This is the information that is in the passage. Every passage has many facts and details.

Directions: Read the passage below. The passage is followed by questions that can be answered by finding facts and details in the passage. Use this passage to answer all the questions on pages 8–10.

A Secret to Share

1   Ming-Lee had a secret place that she had discovered in the woods. It was under an old oak tree. In the summer, it was shady and cool. She liked to lie on her back and watch the sun shining down through the leaves. If there was a breeze, the light seemed to dance.

2   Ming-Lee enjoyed the special smells of the woods. There was the smell of the pine trees. The old leaves that had fallen to the ground had a dusty smell. The moss growing on the north side of the oak tree smelled like the earth. She enjoyed listening to the sounds of the leaves moving in the breeze.

3   Ming-Lee liked to sit quietly. She watched squirrels dart around. She listened to birds sing. She found things that she liked in the woods. Ming-Lee made a box out of pine twigs and leaves and put her special things in it. Her favorite was a tiny black rock that was very shiny.

4   One day Ming-Lee found a little pile of rocks, twigs, and leaves under the oak tree. It almost looked like a little house. There was even an opening that looked like a door. She was angry that someone had come into her special place. But she also was very curious.

5   The next day, there was another little house. Ming-Lee stared at the strange little houses. Where had they come from? Suddenly, she heard the sound of someone walking through the woods. Then she saw another little girl walking toward her.

6   "Hi." said the other girl.

7   "Did you make these?" Ming-Lee asked, pointing to the little twig and leaf houses.

8   The girl nodded her head. "They're fairy houses."

9   "What's a fairy house?" asked Ming-Lee.

10   "A house you build, so that fairies can to come and live in it," said the girl.

11   "I'm Ming-Lee. What's your name?"

12   "I'm Grace. We just moved here. I was walking behind my house and I saw this place."

13   "You can come in," said Ming-Lee.

14   Ming-Lee stretched out on the ground and looked up through the leaves. Grace did too. They lay there quietly. Ming-Lee liked that Grace didn't mind being quiet.

15   The girls played together all afternoon. Grace showed Ming-Lee how to make a fairy house. Ming-Lee decided that sharing her secret place with Grace made it even better.

Modeled Instruction

Directions: Below is an example of a question that can be answered by recalling facts and details. Follow the strategy that is explained to help choose the correct answer.

---

1 Where is Ming-Lee's secret place?

Ⓐ in a fairy land

Ⓑ in her house

Ⓒ in the woods

Ⓓ in Grace's house

Strategy: Use key words from the question to help you find the answer. The key words for this question are "secret place." Find those words in the story and read that part of the story. This will help you know what the answer is.

Use this strategy to decide which answer is correct.

 Ⓐ in a fairy land

Grace says that the little houses are fairy houses. The words "secret place" and the word "fairy" are in paragraph 15, the last paragraph. But it does not say that Ming-Lee's secret place is in a fairy land. *Choice "A" cannot be the correct answer.*

 Ⓒ in the woods

The words "secret place" and the words "in the woods" are in paragraph 1, the first paragraph. Facts in the paragraph tell you that Ming-Lee's secret place is in the woods. *Choice "C" must be the correct answer.*

 Ⓑ in her house

There are no facts about Ming-Lee's house. *Choice "B" cannot be the correct answer.*

 Ⓓ in Grace's house

Grace walks behind her house to find Ming-Lee's secret place. But the story does not have any facts about Grace's house. *Choice "D" cannot be the correct answer.*

Guided Instruction

Directions: Use the hints to answer the questions below. For question 2, you must choose the correct answer. For question 3, you will need to write out your answer.

2 **What did Ming-Lee use to make a box?**

(A) cards

(B) paper

(C) twigs and leaves

(D) wood and nails

Hint: Look for the word "box." Read that part of the story to find the facts you need to answer the question.

3 **What did Ming-Lee see after she heard the sound of someone walking in the woods?**

_____

_____

_____

_____

_____

_____

_____

_____

_____

_____

_____

_____

Hint: The words "heard the sound" are in paragraph 5. Read this paragraph again. Find the facts you need to answer the question.

Independent Study

Directions: Answer the following questions on your own. For questions 4, 5, and 6, choose the correct answer. For question 7, you must write out your answer.

4 What strange thing did Ming-Lee see in the woods?

Ⓐ a tree

Ⓑ a clearing

Ⓒ a gray squirrel eating red berries

Ⓓ a pile of rocks, twigs, and leaves

5 Ming-Lee finds out that the strange thing is—

Ⓐ a squirrel house

Ⓑ a fairy house

Ⓒ a treasure box

Ⓓ an ant house

6 What does Grace teach Ming-Lee?

Ⓐ how to find the secret place

Ⓑ how to stay very quiet

Ⓒ how to make a fairy house

Ⓓ how to find Grace's house

7 What is something that Ming-Lee likes about Grace?

_____

_____

_____

_____

_____

_____

Skill 2: Main Idea

The main idea is what the whole passage is about. A passage may be about more than one thing. The main idea is what it is mostly about. The main idea of a paragraph or sentence is what that paragraph or sentence is mostly about.

Directions: Read this passage. The questions after the passage ask about main ideas. Use the passage to answer all the questions on pages 13–15.

You Can Smell When It's Around

1   "Skunk" is a Native American word, so this animal has been around for a long time. You probably know what a skunk looks like. And you most likely know what skunk spray smells like. What else do you know about skunks?

2   A skunk is about the size of a cat. Its fur is long, and it has a bushy tail. Skunks have five toes on each foot, and long claws that they use for digging. The striped skunk is the most common. It is black with two white stripes on its back. The spotted skunk is also black and white. There are hooded skunks that have thick fur around their necks. The hognose skunk has a nose that looks like a pig's nose.

3   These small furry animals can live almost anywhere. Skunks like to live in the woods. They also like deserts and grassy areas. They live in most of the United States and in parts of Canada.

4   A skunk will eat just about anything. It likes vegetables, and bugs. It likes birds' eggs. It will even eat mice and rats. When a skunk eats insects, it helps us. It keeps those pests out of our gardens!

5   Why do skunks spray? A skunk will spray when it thinks it is in danger. First the skunk will stamp its front feet. If that doesn't work, then the skunk will spray. The spray comes from under the skunk's tail. If the spray gets in the eyes of an enemy, it will sting. It also has a very strong odor that is hard to get rid of.

6   Some people have skunks as pets. They can be funny and cuddly. Skunks that are pets are fixed, so they cannot spray their owners! Do you think you would like a pet skunk?

Modeled Instruction

Directions: Below is an example of a question that can be answered by identifying the main idea of the passage. Follow the strategy that is explained to help choose the correct answer.

---

1 **The name of a story is its title. What would be another good title for this story?**

Ⓐ "Small Animals"

Ⓑ "Helpful Skunks"

Ⓒ "Different Kinds of Pets"

Ⓓ "A Closer Look at Skunks"

Strategy: A good title can tell a reader the main idea of a passage. You need to think about all of the information you read to tell what the main idea of the passage is. Ask yourself, "What is the passage <u>mostly</u> about?"

Use this strategy to decide which answer is correct.

Ⓐ **"Small Animals"**

A skunk is a small animal. Mice and rats are also mentioned one time, but that is all. The story does not tell about those animals. It is mostly about one animal. *Choice "A" cannot be correct.*

Ⓒ **"Different Kinds of Pets"**

The word "pets" is in the last paragraph. But that is the only place, so it is not the main idea. *Choice "C" cannot be the correct answer.*

Ⓑ **"Helpful Skunks"**

The story says that skunks can be helpful when they eat insects. But that is all it says about skunks being helpful. *Choice "B" cannot be correct.*

Ⓓ **"A Closer Look at Skunks"**

All of the paragraphs are about skunks. Each paragraph tells you something about them. *Choice "D" must be the correct answer.*

Guided Instruction

Directions: Use the hints to answer the questions below. For question 2, you must choose the correct answer. For question 3, you will need to write out your answer.

---

2 Paragraph 3 in the story tells mostly about—

   Ⓐ the United States

   Ⓑ deserts and grassy areas

   Ⓒ where skunks live

   Ⓓ the woods

Hint: To answer this question you only need to look at the paragraph 3. Think about what facts can be found in this paragraph. Ask yourself what most of these facts are about.

---

3 What is the main idea in paragraph 4? Remember to list the facts that are about the main idea.

_____

_____

_____

_____

_____

_____

_____

_____

_____

_____

_____

_____

Hint: Think about the facts that are in paragraph 4. What are all the facts about? This is the main idea. Use the facts in your answer.

Independent Study

Directions: Answer the following questions on your own. For questions 4, 5, and 6, choose the correct answer. For question 7, you must write out your answer.

4 This passage is mostly about—

Ⓐ skunks

Ⓑ skunk spray

Ⓒ where skunks live

Ⓓ what skunks eat

5 What is the main idea of paragraph 2 in the story?

Ⓐ how skunks walk

Ⓑ the color of skunks

Ⓒ what skunks look like

Ⓓ how skunks are like cats

6 Which fact below would fit best in paragraph 5 of the story?

Ⓐ A skunk's teeth are quite sharp.

Ⓑ Skunk babies are called kittens.

Ⓒ A skunk can spray about ten to fifteen inches.

Ⓓ Skunks' claws are very much like dogs' claws.

7 What would make a good title for paragraph 5 in the story? Explain why you think this would make a good title.

_____

_____

_____

_____

_____

_____

_____

_____

Skill 3: Sequence

Sequence is the order in which things or events happen. Things in the passage happen in a certain order. Each thing happens before, after, or at the same time as another thing.

Directions: Read the passage below. The passage is followed by questions that can be answered by telling the sequence. Use this passage to answer all the questions on pages 18–20.

Going through the Changes

1   Animals can be divided into different groups. Fish belong in one group of animals. Reptiles belong in another group. Then there is a group of animals that are a little bit like fish and a little bit like reptiles. The animals in this group are called amphibians.

2   "Amphibian" means "both ways." Most of these animals live part of their life in the water. And they live part of their life on land.

3   Frogs and toads are in this group. So are salamanders and newts. Animals in this group can look very, very different from each other. But they are the same in some ways.

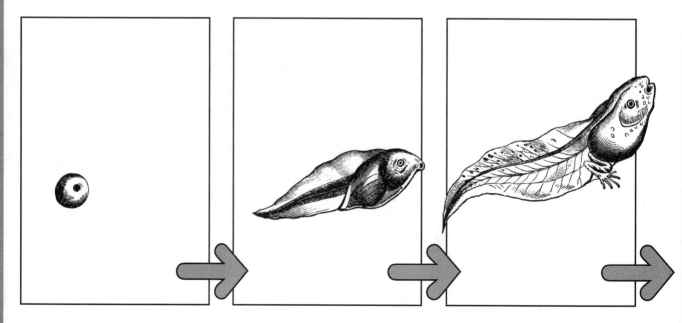

4   All amphibians have a backbone. And all of these animals are cold blooded. That means that their bodies get hot when they are in a hot place and cold when they are in a cold place. They all breathe air through their lungs and skin. Most of them are born from eggs and most of the eggs have no shell. The eggs are laid in wet places. When the babies are born they do not look like their parents, but they will later.

5   Amphibians change a lot as they grow. A frog begins as a tiny egg. Then it becomes a tadpole with a very long tail and no legs. It breathes with gills. Then the tadpole's legs start to grow and its tail disappears. It starts using lungs to breathe. At last, the tadpole is a frog that has four legs. It can leave the water and walk on land.

6   One kind of frog carries its eggs on its back. The eggs turn into tadpoles. Later, the tadpoles are ready to swim. Then they are dropped off in the water.

7   A salamander starts as a tiny egg. As it grows it gets little legs and a tail. It breathes with gills like fish do. Then its legs grow longer. It grows lungs, and the gills disappear. Now, it can leave the water and live on land.

8   Some salamanders change again! They live on land for a while. Later, they go back to the water to live.

9   Change is what amphibians are all about!

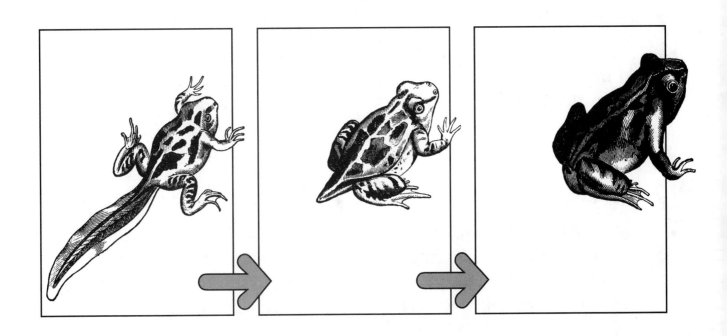

Modeled Instruction

Directions: Below is an example of a question that can be answered by identifying the sequence of events. Follow the strategy that is explained to help choose the correct answer.

---

1 What does a frog do <u>after</u> it grows four legs?

  Ⓐ It lives in an egg.

  Ⓑ It lives on the land.

  Ⓒ It grows a longer tail.

  Ⓓ It goes back into the water.

Strategy: To answer a question about the order in which things happened, it can help to make a chart. Read the story again and put the facts in the chart. Finish these charts before you answer the questions for this story.

	Frog	Salamander
First		
Then		
Then		
Then		
Then		
Then		

Use this strategy to decide which answer is correct.

 Ⓐ It lives in an egg.

Your chart should show that a frog begins as an egg. An egg does not have legs. So, *choice "A" cannot be correct.*

 Ⓒ It grows a longer tail.

Look at your chart. When it has a tail, a frog is still a tadpole. It does not have legs yet. So, *choice "C" cannot be the correct answer.*

 Ⓑ It lives on the land.

The last box in your chart should show that the frog is living on land. It has four legs before it does this. So, *choice "B" must be the correct answer.*

 Ⓓ It goes back into the water.

Look at your chart. It does not say that frogs go back into the water to live. So, *choice "D" cannot be correct.*

Guided Instruction

Directions: Use the hints to answer the questions below. For question 2, you must choose the correct answer. For question 3, you will need to write out your answer.

2 Which of the following happens to a salamander first?

Ⓐ It is a tiny egg.

Ⓑ It lives on land.

Ⓒ It breathes with gills.

Ⓓ It grows legs and lungs.

Hint: Use the information in your chart to answer this question. Which thing happens first?

3 List three things that happen to a frog after it is an egg.

_____

_____

_____

_____

_____

_____

_____

_____

_____

_____

_____

_____

Hint: Look at your chart to find all of the things that happen to a frog after it is an egg. Think about all the facts in the story.

Independent Study

Directions: Answer the following questions on your own. For questions 4, 5, and 6, choose the correct answer. For question 7, you must write out your answer.

---

4 Look at the chart about the salamander.

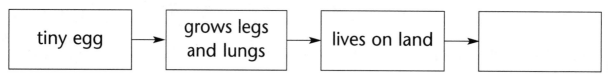

Which choice should be placed in the empty box to complete the chart about a salamander?

Ⓐ loses its tail

Ⓑ legs grow shorter

Ⓒ breathes with gills

Ⓓ returns to the water

---

5 What happens to a frog before it loses its tail, but after it is an egg?

Ⓐ It lays eggs.

Ⓑ It lives on land.

Ⓒ It has four legs.

Ⓓ It breathes with gills.

6 Which fact comes first in this story?

Ⓐ All amphibians have a backbone.

Ⓑ Some salamanders change again.

Ⓒ Frogs and toads are in this group.

Ⓓ The eggs are laid in wet places.

---

7 List three things that happen to the frog eggs that grow on the parent's back. Describe what happens in the correct order.

_____

_____

_____

_____

A Skill 4: Language and Vocabulary

Words, phrases, and sentences are used in every passage. Language is used to tell about ideas. Words and phrases have certain meanings. Sometimes there is more than one meaning. The meaning often depends on how the words are used.

Directions: Read the poem below. The poem is followed by questions that can be answered by thinking about the words, phrases, and sentences. Use this poem to answer all the questions on pages 22–24.

The Swing
by Robert Louis Stevenson

1   How do you like to go up in a swing,
2   Up in the air so blue?
3   Oh, I do think it the *pleasantest* thing
4   Ever a child can do!

5   Up in the air and over the wall,
6   Till I can see so wide,
7   River and trees and *cattle* and all
8   Over the *countryside*—

9   Till I look down on the garden green,
10   *Down* on the roof so brown—
11   Up in the air I go flying again,
12   Up in the air and down!

Modeled Instruction

Directions: Below is an example of a question that can be answered by analyzing language in the poem. Follow the strategy that is explained to help choose the correct answer.

---

1 In line 3 the word
pleasantest **means—**

Ⓐ hardest

Ⓑ scariest

Ⓒ most lonely

Ⓓ most enjoyable

Strategy: Thinking about how a word is used can help you to understand its meaning. Think about how this word is used in the poem. Sometimes other words can give you clues about the meaning.

Use this strategy to decide which answer is correct.

 Ⓐ **hardest**

The person who wrote this poem likes to swing. The poem says that when you swing you go flying up high and back down again. It is something you can do many times. It is not a hard thing to do. *Choice "A" is not the best possible meaning for the word.*

 Ⓒ **most lonely**

The poet may be swinging alone. But that does not mean that the poet is lonely. There is nothing in the poem to make you think that the writer is lonely. *Choice "C" is not the best possible meaning for the word.*

 Ⓑ **scariest**

The way the poet talks about swinging, it does not sound scary. The poet seems to be having fun. *Choice "B" is not the best possible meaning for the word.*

 Ⓓ **most enjoyable**

It sounds as if the poet is having a fine time swinging. It is something that the poet likes to do. *Choice "D" is the correct answer.*

Guided Instruction

Directions: Use the hints to answer the questions below. For question 2, you must choose the correct answer. For question 3, you will need to write out your answer.

2 The phrase "Up in the air and over the wall," seems to mean—

(A) the swing has fallen over the wall

(B) the swing is so high the poet can see over the wall

(C) the poet used the swing to jump over the wall

(D) the swing is on the other side of the wall

Hint: Compare words in each answer choice with the words in the question. Which answer choice has the same meaning as the words in the question?

3 What do you think the words "up in the air so blue" means?

_____

_____

_____

_____

_____

_____

_____

_____

_____

Hint: Read the part of the poem where these words are used. What does the poem tell you about what the poet can see? What kind of day is it?

Independent Study

Directions: Answer the following questions on your own. For questions 4, 5, and 6, choose the correct answer. For question 7, you must write out your answer.

4 *Cattle* are—

Ⓐ cows

Ⓑ houses

Ⓒ flowers

Ⓓ swings

5 Read the different meanings for the word *down.*

1. from standing to sitting

2. a feeling of sadness

3. a bird's soft feathers

4. from a higher to a lower place

Which meaning best fits the way the word *down* is used in the last line of the poem?

Ⓐ meaning 1

Ⓑ meaning 2

Ⓒ meaning 3

Ⓓ meaning 4

6 Which words help the reader know what the word *countryside* means?

Ⓐ the garden green

Ⓑ the roof so brown

Ⓒ river and trees and cattle

Ⓓ up in the air and over the wall

7 In line 6 what does the poet mean by "I can see so wide"?

_____

_____

_____

_____

_____

_____

_____

_____

_____

_____

_____

_____

Skill 5: Character, Plot, and Setting

These three things are found in every story.

CHARACTER	This is **who** the story is about.
PLOT	This is **what** the story is about.
SETTING	This is **where** and when the events in the story take place.

Directions: Read the passage below. It is followed by questions that can be answered by telling about the characters, plot, and setting. Use this story to answer all the questions on pages 27–29.

1   The sun was shining in the window of Donna's bedroom. It made a patch of warm light on the fluffy white cat lying beside her. Donna patted the cat's soft fur and remembered when she and her brother had found him.

2   They had been playing in the backyard when they heard a soft meowing sound. It was coming from under the shed. The children knelt down and peered into the darkness. They could see a tiny form. Donna wanted to get the kitten out. But her brother, Jake, said, "Let's ask Mom first. Maybe its mother is coming back."

3   Their mother had agreed with Jake. She said, "If the mother doesn't come back by tonight, we'll help the kitten. It's going to be cold when the sun goes down."

4   The children waited. It was hard to listen to the kitten's cries. But they wanted to do the right thing. It began to get dark, and the mother had not returned. "Let's take care of this little baby," their mother said.

5   They got the kitten out of its cold, dirty hiding place. It was white and gray. Jake patted its little round head. It was so young that its eyes were still closed. "This kitten will need a lot of love and care," their mother said. "Are you ready to do that?"

6   "Yes!" they cried. They put a box in Donna's room and placed a heating pad under it. They put a towel in the box. Their mother drove them to the pet store, where they bought cans of milk. It was like the milk the kitten would have been getting from its mother. Every couple of hours, they fed the kitten with a dropper. After each meal they would put the kitten back in the warm box. It was a lot of work.

7   Then one day Donna saw that the kitten's eyes were open just a little. In a few more days, they were opened wide. Soon the kitten was able to climb out of the box. From then on, Donna's bed was his favorite place to sleep.

8   When they took the kitten to see the vet, he said, "You did a wonderful job taking care of him. He's very healthy. This little guy looks great!"

9   That was over two years ago. Now, on Donna's bed, the cat rolled over and put his paw on her face. "Puff, you silly cat," said Donna, "I'm so glad we found you!"

Modeled Instruction

Directions: Below is an example of a question that can be answered by analyzing character, plot, and setting in the passage. Follow the strategy that is explained to help choose the correct answer.

---

1 **Where does <u>most</u> of the story take place?**

Ⓐ at the pet store

Ⓑ in Donna's bedroom

Ⓒ in the vet's office

Ⓓ under the backyard shed

Strategy: To answer questions about a story, it can be helpful to organize the facts in the story. A story map uses boxes and arrows. It shows who is in the story and what they do. It can also show where the story takes place and when things happen. This question is asking you where the story took place.

Use this strategy to decide which answer is correct.

 Ⓐ **at the pet store**

The story says that they bought milk at the pet store. But there is nothing else about the pet store. *Choice "A" cannot be correct.*

 Ⓒ **in the vet's office**

Part of the story takes place in the vet's office. But it is only a small part. Most of the story does not take place there. *Choice "C" cannot be correct.*

 Ⓑ **in Donna's bedroom**

Different things in the story happen in different places, but most of the story happens in one place. The kitten's box was in Donna's room, and the kitten lived there until it could climb out of the box. Then Donna's bed was his favorite spot to sleep. And Donna and the cat are on her bed in the beginning and end of the story. *Choice "B" must be the correct answer.*

 Ⓓ **under the backyard shed**

The children hear the kitten crying, and they find him under the backyard shed. When it starts to get dark, they rescue the kitten from under the shed and bring him in the house. But that is all in one day and it is just the beginning of the story. Many parts of the story happen in other places. *Choice "D" cannot be correct.*

Guided Instruction

Directions: Use the hints to answer the questions below. For question 2, you must choose the correct answer. For question 3, you will need to write out your answer.

---

2 **What can you tell about Jake and Donna from reading the passage?**

- Ⓐ They care about animals.

- Ⓑ They would rather have a dog.

- Ⓒ They do not get along very well.

- Ⓓ They have saved many kittens.

Hint: Think about what Jake and Donna did in the story. The things that the people in a story do or say can tell you a lot about them.

---

3 **Tell what this story is about. Explain what happens in the beginning, the middle, and the end of the story.**

_____

_____

_____

_____

_____

_____

_____

_____

_____

_____

_____

_____

Hint: To tell what the story is about you only need to tell the important facts. Think about what information is important to know.

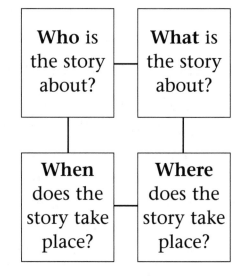

Who is the story about?	**What** is the story about?
When does the story take place?	**Where** does the story take place?

Independent Study

Directions: Answer the following questions on your own. For questions 4, 5, and 6, choose the correct answer. For question 7, you must write out your answer.

4 The children's mother can best be described as—

Ⓐ angry

Ⓑ quiet

Ⓒ kind

Ⓓ funny

5 Where is the kitten when the children find him?

Ⓐ under a shed

Ⓑ at the vet's

Ⓒ at the pet store

Ⓓ in a bedroom

6 What happens when the children find the kitten?

Ⓐ They keep playing ball in the backyard.

Ⓑ They feed him warm milk and cat food.

Ⓒ They take him into their mother's bedroom.

Ⓓ They ask their mother what they should do.

7 How would you describe Donna? Include two things that show the kind of person she is.

_____

_____

_____

_____

_____

_____

_____

A Skill 6: Cause and Effect

The cause leads to the effect.

CAUSE	*The wind blows hard.*
EFFECT	*The tree falls down.*

Directions: Read the passage below. The passage is followed by questions that can be answered by knowing the cause and effect. Use this passage to answer all the questions on pages 32–34.

 # Take Care of Yourself

1   Wash your hands. Cover your mouth when you sneeze. Take a shower. Brush your teeth. Be sure to floss. Eat your vegetables. It's time for bed.

2   Yes, you have heard these things many times. You know that you should stay clean. You know that you should eat good food and get lots of exercise. You know that sleep is good for you. But do you understand why all these things are so important?

3   Most of the things you touch every day have some germs on them. Germs are everywhere. Not all germs can make you sick, but many germs can. If you get germs in your eyes, your eyes can get infected. If germs get in a cut, the cut can get infected. Germs can cause you to have a headache or a fever.

4   When you sneeze, germs come out of your nose. When you touch your nose with your hand, the germs get on your hand. Then, if you touch something else, the germs get on that. When another person touches that same thing, they can get your germs. They may catch your cold. That's why it is important to wash your hands often with warm water and soap. Taking a bath or shower gets germs off your body.

5   Brushing your teeth protects your mouth from germs that can cause cavities. Flossing removes food and germs from between your teeth. These germs can make your gums sore.

6   Walking, running, and playing make your muscles strong. Strong muscles help you stand up straight and move easily. Exercise makes your bones strong, too.

7   Your body needs a lot of water. When you drink water, it helps your body to get rid of waste. This helps your body work better, and it makes you feel better, too.

8   Good foods help your body grow and give you energy. They make your bones and teeth strong. They make your skin healthy. Chips, soda, and candy don't help your body. If you ate only that kind of food, you would have less energy. Your hair would not shine. Your teeth and bones would become weak. You would not look or feel very well.

9   Rest is very important, because it helps your body get ready for each new day. When you are tired, you have less energy. It can be hard to think.

10   So take care of your body. You'll look better. And you'll enjoy yourself more!

Modeled Instruction

Directions: Below is an example of a question that can be answered by recognizing cause and effect. Follow the strategy that is explained to help choose the correct answer.

---

1 What can cause your gums to be sore?

- (A) not getting enough sleep
- (B) brushing your teeth
- (C) eating too many healthful foods
- (D) leaving germs between your teeth

Strategy: Look for key words in the question to help you figure out where to look for the answer. Look for the words "sore" and "gums." Read that part of the story.

Use this strategy to decide which answer is correct.

 (A) not getting enough sleep

This question asks you to find the cause. The effect is sore gums. The words "sore" and "gums" are in paragraph 5. There is nothing in that paragraph about sleep. *Choice "A" cannot be correct.*

 (C) eating too many healthful foods

In paragraph 8 it says that eating healthful foods is good for you. So, eating healthful foods does not cause sore gums. Also, the words "sore" and "gums" are not in paragraph 6. *Choice "C" cannot be correct.*

 (B) brushing your teeth

The passage talks about brushing your teeth in paragraph 5. The words "sore" and "gums" are in this same paragraph. The story tells you that brushing your teeth is healthy. But brushing cannot reach the germs between your teeth. You have to brush your teeth and floss them to get all the germs. *Choice "B" is not correct.*

 (D) leaving germs between your teeth

Paragraph 5 tells what happens when you don't floss. Your toothbrush can't reach the germs in the spaces between your teeth. If you don't floss, the germs stay there. The effect of not flossing is sore gums. And the words "sore" and "gums" are in this paragraph. *Choice "D" is the correct answer.*

Guided Instruction

Directions: Use the hints to answer the questions below. For question 2, you must choose the correct answer. For question 3, you will need to write out your answer.

2 What happens when you walk, run, or play?

- Ⓐ You catch a cold.
- Ⓑ You eat more chips.
- Ⓒ Your muscles get stronger.
- Ⓓ You cannot think very well.

Hint: Walking, running, and playing are the cause of something. Look for the words "walk, run, and play." That will help you find the part of the story you need to read to find the answer.

3 What can cause you to have trouble thinking?

Hint: Having trouble thinking is the effect of something else that happens. Look through the story to find the cause.

Independent Study

Directions: Answer the following questions on your own. For questions 4, 5, and 6, choose the correct answer. For question 7, you must write out your answer.

4 **What happens when you take a shower?**

   Ⓐ Your gums get sore.

   Ⓑ Your muscles get stronger.

   Ⓒ You wash germs off your body.

   Ⓓ You touch germs that make you sick.

5 **What may happen if you sneeze on your hand and then rub your eye?**

   Ⓐ You may get an infected cut.

   Ⓑ You may need a lot of sleep.

   Ⓒ You may get an eye infection.

   Ⓓ You may need to drink a lot of water.

6 **If you take good care of your body—**

   Ⓐ you will spread more germs

   Ⓑ you will be able to drink more soda

   Ⓒ you will not need to sleep as much

   Ⓓ you will feel better and be stronger

7 **If you ate only chips, soda, and candy, how would you feel and look?**

_____

_____

_____

_____

_____

_____

_____

_____

_____

ASkill 7: Compare and Contrast

Compare means to tell how things are alike. Contrast means to tell how things are different. You can compare and contrast people, places, or things that happen.

Directions: Read the passage below. The passage is followed by questions that can be answered by comparing or contrasting. Use this passage to answer all the questions on pages 37–39.

1   People like to catch them and eat them. And some people like to keep them as pets. There are more than 20,000 different kinds of fish in the world. There might be some that no one has ever seen! All fish live in water and they all breathe through gills. Fish have a backbone. After that, not all fish are the same at all!

2   There are three groups of fish: jawless fish, sharks and shark-like fish, and bony fish. Some live in the ocean because they need salt water. Freshwater fish live in streams, lakes, and ponds.

3   The chart below shows how some fish are alike and different. Across the top of the chart are Fish Facts. Down the left side are Fish Names. Look at the fish name on the left. Then look at each box in the line next to it. If there is a dot in the box it means that the fact is true for that fish.

FISH NAMES	FISH FACTS						
	Has Gills	Has a Backbone	Lives in Fresh Water	Lives in Salt Water	Has Bones	Has Jaws	Has Scales
Trout	*	*	*		*	*	*
Shark	*	*		*		*	
Tuna	*	*		*	*	*	*
Guppy	*	*	*		*	*	*
Eel	*	*	*	*	*	*	
Hagfish	*	*		*			
Goldfish	*	*	*		*	*	*

4   For example, look at "Trout." The first box next to "Trout" has a dot. The fact above that box is "Has Gills." A trout has gills.

5   Find the fact "Lives in Salt Water," and then look at the boxes under it. Find the first box that has a dot. Now look over to Fish Name to see which fish it is. It is a shark.

6   There are some very unusual fish. Some fish are called flatfish. They are much flatter than other fish. And both eyes are on the left side of the body!

7   Many animals in the ocean are not fish. The whale is a mammal, because it has warm blood. Dolphins are not fish either. Like whales, they need to come to the surface to breathe air. And the starfish has no backbone, so it is not a fish!

Modeled Instruction

Directions: Below is an example of a question that can be answered by comparing and contrasting information in the passage. Follow the strategy that is explained to help choose the correct answer.

> **1 Which of these is something that is true for all fish?**
>
> Ⓐ All fish are flat.
>
> Ⓑ All fish have scales.
>
> Ⓒ All fish live in the ocean.
>
> Ⓓ All fish live in water.

Strategy: Making lists can help you to compare and contrast. You can make one list that tells how things are alike and another to tell how they are different. These lists can be used to help answer questions that ask you to compare and contrast.

Use this strategy to decide which answer is correct.

 Ⓐ All fish are flat.

Paragraph 6 tells you about flatfish. It talks about only one kind of fish. It says "some fish are called flatfish." This means that not all fish are called flatfish. Therefore, *choice "A" cannot be correct.*

 Ⓒ All fish live in the ocean.

Many fish do live in the ocean. But the ocean is salty. Only saltwater fish live there. Other fish live in fresh water. Since some fish live in fresh water, *choice "C" cannot be correct.*

 Ⓑ All fish have scales.

Look at the chart. It shows you that some fish do have scales. But not all of the fish have scales. Since some fish do not have scales, *choice "B" cannot be correct.*

 Ⓓ All fish live in water.

The first paragraph tells you that all fish do live in water. It is one of the things that is true for all fish. Therefore, *choice "D" is the correct answer.*

Guided Instruction

Directions: Use the hints to answer the questions below. For question 2, you must choose the correct answer. For question 3, you will need to write out your answer.

2 What is one way in which sharks are different from tunas?

(A) Sharks have jaws.

(B) Sharks live in the ocean.

(C) Sharks do not have scales.

(D) Sharks breathe through gills.

Hint: All of the details listed are true, but only one tells how sharks and tunas are different. Look at the chart. Which detail is true about sharks, but NOT true about tunas? You can make a Venn Diagram to help you answer this question or you can use the list that you made for question 1.

3 How are sharks and eels alike?

_____

_____

_____

_____

_____

_____

_____

_____

_____

_____

Hint: Look at the chart. Read the information given about each fish. Compare the facts. Tell how the two are alike.

Independent Study

Directions: Answer the following questions on your own. For questions 4, 5, and 6, choose the correct answer. For question 7, you must write out your answer.

4 **Which fish can live in both fresh water and salt water?**

Ⓐ eels

Ⓑ skates

Ⓒ guppies

Ⓓ goldfish

5 **How is the hagfish different from every other fish in the chart?**

Ⓐ It has gills.

Ⓑ It has a backbone.

Ⓒ It does not have jaws.

Ⓓ It does not have bones.

6 **Which is NOT true for all the freshwater fish shown on the chart?**

Ⓐ They all have bones.

Ⓑ They all have jaws.

Ⓒ They all have gills.

Ⓓ They all have scales.

7 **What is one way that whales and dolphins are different from fish?**

_____

_____

_____

_____

_____

_____

_____

_____

_____

_____

_____

Skill 8: Facts and Opinions

It is important to be able to tell the difference between facts and opinions.

FACT   A fact is a statement that is true.
There are 50 states in the United States.

OPINION   An opinion is a statement that someone believes is true.
My state is the most beautiful.

Directions: Read the passage below. The passage is followed by questions that can be answered by telling fact from opinion. Use this passage to answer all of the questions on pages 42–44.

Hairy Legs

They are the largest spiders in the world. They can have a body that is three inches long. Their legs can be ten inches across. They have hair all over their body. What are they? They are tarantulas. And they are scary-looking! 1

A tarantula is a spider. Like all spiders, it has eight legs. Its body has three parts. Some of these spiders are big, but some are quite small. They can be many colors, but most are brown. Some have red spots, and some have bands of orange on their legs. Others have some stripes. But I don't think their colors make them pretty. They are still creepy bugs to me! 2

3   Many people like tarantulas. They have them as pets and keep them in tanks. They should get a dog or a cat instead.

4   In the wild, tarantulas live in many different places. Some live in the desert. Some live in the jungle and others live in deep holes that they dig in the ground.

5   Spiders have eight eyes. But tarantulas cannot see well. The hairs on their legs help them tell where things are. They can taste with their mouth. They can also taste with other parts of their body.

6   Some tarantulas can match their color to the area around them. This makes them hard to see and keeps them safe. They also can drop their hairs. The hairs have sharp ends that can hurt. A tarantula will bite, too. A bite will probably not kill a person. But it will be painful!

7   A hungry tarantula will eat any animal it can catch. It might be a bird or a mouse or a bug. It could be a lizard or a snake or another spider. Tarantulas bite their prey. Poison from their fangs kills it. Then they suck out all the fluids. It does not sound very nice, but this is how the tarantula gets its food.

8   The babies come from eggs. New spiders stay near their mother at first. But soon they are on their own.

9   A tarantula sheds its furry skin as it grows. The empty skin looks just like the spider. I would not want to run into the skin or the spider!

Modeled Instruction

Directions: Below is an example of a question that can be answered by distinguishing fact from opinion in the passage. Follow the strategy that is explained to help choose the correct answer.

---

1 Which sentence from the passage is a fact?

  Ⓐ "The hairs have sharp ends that can hurt."

  Ⓑ "But I don't think their colors make them pretty."

  Ⓒ "They are still creepy bugs to me!"

  Ⓓ "I would not want to run into the skin or the spider!"

Strategy: To tell if a statement is a fact or an opinion, think about what you can prove. Statements that can be proven are facts. If a statement cannot be proven it is an opinion. Use the information in the passage to help determine which statements are facts and which are opinions.

Use this strategy to decide which answer is correct.

Ⓐ "The hairs have sharp ends that can hurt."

Science books tell you that spiders have hairs with sharp ends that can hurt. Since you can prove this, it must be a fact. Therefore, *choice "A" must be the correct answer.*

Ⓒ "They are still creepy bugs to me!"

This is how the author feels. Since there is no way to prove that this is true, it must be an opinion. Therefore, *choice "C" cannot be correct.*

Ⓑ "But I don't think their colors make them pretty."

What someone thinks is always an opinion. This statement tells what the author thinks. You can't prove that it is true or false, so it is an opinion. Therefore, *choice "B" cannot be correct.*

Ⓓ "I would not want to run into the skin or the spider!"

The author would not like to see the skin or the spider. Someone else might think it was interesting. Since you cannot prove whether people want to see this or not, *choice "D" cannot be correct.*

Guided Instruction

Directions: Use the hints to answer the questions below. For question 2, you must choose the correct answer. For question 3, you will need to write out your answer.

---

2 **Which sentence from the passage states an opinion?**

Ⓐ "A tarantula is a spider."

Ⓑ "Many people like tarantulas."

Ⓒ "Its body has three parts."

Ⓓ "Others have some stripes."

Hint: Read the answer choices one at a time. To find the statement that is an opinion, ask yourself which is the statement that you cannot prove.

---

3 **Read the following sentence from the passage:**

"In the wild, tarantulas live in many different places."

Is this statement an example of a fact or an opinion? Explain your answer.

Hint: Think about what makes a statement a fact or an opinion. Ask yourself if the statement tells about something that is true or something that someone believes is true.

_____

_____

_____

_____

_____

_____

_____

_____

Independent Study

Directions: Answer the following questions on your own. For questions 4, 5, and 6, choose the correct answer. For question 7, you must write out your answer.

4 **Which sentence from the passage is NOT a fact?**

Ⓐ "A hungry tarantula will eat any animal it can catch."

Ⓑ "They should get a dog or a cat instead."

Ⓒ "They can taste with their mouth."

Ⓓ "Some live in the desert."

5 **Which sentence from the passage is an opinion?**

Ⓐ "And they are scary-looking!"

Ⓑ "Poison from their fangs kills it."

Ⓒ "They have hair all over their body."

Ⓓ "Their legs can be ten inches across."

6 **Which sentence from the passage contains both a fact AND an opinion?**

Ⓐ "New spiders stay near their mother at first."

Ⓑ "But I don't think their colors make them pretty."

Ⓒ "It does not sound very nice, but this is how the tarantula gets its food."

Ⓓ "Some tarantulas can match their color to the area around them."

7 **Read the following sentence from the passage:**

"A bite will probably not kill a person."

Is this statement an example of a fact or an opinion? Explain your answer.

_____

_____

_____

_____

A Skill 9: Predict Outcomes

This means to figure out what will happen next or in the future. The exact information is not in the passage. But the facts and details may help tell what will happen.

Directions: Read the story below. The story is followed by questions that can be answered by predicting outcomes. Use this story to answer all of the questions on pages 47–49.

Getting Ready

1   "Sam, do you know what tomorrow is?" asked his mother.

2   "It's Dad's birthday!" cried Sam. He knew that his father's birthday was the next day. Sam had been getting ready all week. He had already made his dad a birthday card. But now he had a new idea for a card. He liked his new idea better.

3   Sam had also talked to his mother about a present. He wanted to get a gift for his father to unwrap. Sam loved to wrap presents. He liked to choose the paper and tie the ribbon. And he loved to watch people unwrap the presents he gave them.

4   Sam's father liked to play golf. Sam knew his father needed some more golf balls. Sam had counted the money in his bank and he had enough to buy the golf balls.

5   One of Sam's favorite things was eating birthday cake. His mother told him that he could help make the cake. He had been learning to crack eggs. He was very careful. He did not break the yolk. And he did not let any of the shell fall into the bowl. He was getting to be an expert egg cracker.

6   "What is Dad's favorite kind of cake?" Sam asked his mother.

7   "Your dad likes yellow cake with chocolate frosting," she said. "He always wants the same kind of cake. And he always says the same thing when he sees it."

8   "What's that?" asked Sam.

9   His mother smiled. "He says," she paused and pretended to be Sam's father, "And what kind of cake do we have here?"

10   "It's yellow!" cried Sam. "And it's got chocolate frosting!"

11   "That's right. And we need to do some shopping today so we can make that cake. We will go as soon as I am done cleaning up in the kitchen. Make sure you clean your room, too," she added.

12   Sam wanted some time to work on his new idea. He would have to hurry. He ran up to his room. He felt very excited. The whole day was going to be a lot of fun!

Modeled Instruction

Directions: Below is an example of a question that can be answered by using information from the passage to predict an outcome. Follow the strategy that is explained to help choose the correct answer.

---

1 What will Sam probably do first when he gets upstairs?

- Ⓐ play a game
- Ⓑ find some golf balls
- Ⓒ take a nap
- Ⓓ clean his room

Strategy: Do not look for the answer in the passage. Instead look for details that will help you to make a prediction. Try to find details in the passage that are related in some way to the question. Ask yourself what these details suggest will happen.

Use this strategy to decide which answer is correct.

 Ⓐ play a game

Details in the passage explain that Sam wants to hurry. He wants to have time to work on his new idea before he and his mother leave for the store. It does not make sense that he would take the time to play a game. Therefore, *choice "A" cannot be correct.*

 Ⓒ take a nap

Again, the details in the passage suggest that Sam wants to hurry. There are no details that suggest that Sam is tired. It does not make sense that he would take a nap now. Therefore, *choice "C" cannot be correct.*

 Ⓑ find some golf balls

Details in the passage tell you that Sam has enough money to buy some golf balls. It does not suggest that Sam will find the golf balls in his room. Therefore, *choice "B" cannot be correct.*

 Ⓓ clean his room

Sam's mother tells him that he needs to clean his room. He knows he needs to hurry if he wants to have time to work on his new idea. So it makes sense that he will clean his room right away. Therefore, *choice "D" must be correct.*

Guided Instruction

Directions: Use the hints to answer the questions below. For question 2, you must choose the correct answer. For question 3, you will need to write out your answer.

2 **You can tell that Sam will probably—**

(A) give his father the first card that he made

(B) give his father the new card that he wants to make

(C) not give his father a birthday card

(D) buy a birthday card when he goes to the store

Hint: Look for details in the passage that suggest what Sam is thinking about the card that he made. What do the details suggest that he will do?

3 **What will Sam's gift for his father probably be? Use details from the passage to support your answer.**

_____

_____

_____

_____

_____

_____

_____

_____

_____

_____

Hint: Read the parts of the passage that mention Sam's idea for a birthday gift. Use these details to help you predict what he will give his father.

Independent Study

Directions: Answer the following questions on your own. For questions 4, 5, and 6, choose the correct answer. For question 7, you must write out your answer.

4 **From the passage you can tell that—**

Ⓐ Sam's father will not eat any cake

Ⓑ Sam's father is good at golf

Ⓒ there will be a party for Sam's father

Ⓓ there will not be any cake left for Sam

5 **What will Sam probably do after he buys his present?**

Ⓐ He will wrap it.

Ⓑ He will ask his mother to wrap it.

Ⓒ He will play with the present.

Ⓓ He will ask his mother for more money.

6 **How do you think Sam will help his mother when they make the cake?**

Ⓐ He will crack the eggs.

Ⓑ He will sift the flour.

Ⓒ He will frost the cake.

Ⓓ He will make the frosting.

7 **What kind of cake will Sam and his mother most likely make? Use details from the passage to support your answer.**

_____

_____

_____

_____

_____

_____

_____

_____

_____

Skill 10: Reach Conclusions

Conclusions are based on facts found in the passage. Decisions are made about what the facts mean.

Directions: Read the passage below. The passage is followed by questions that can be answered by reaching conclusions. Use this passage to answer all of the questions on pages 52–54.

Hans Christian Andersen

1   Have you ever heard the story "The Ugly Duckling"? It is a story written long ago by a man named Hans Christian Andersen who wrote many fairy tales. People all over the world have read them.

2   Hans's early life was difficult. His family was very poor. His father made shoes and his mother did washing for other families. This very tall boy was interested in things that did not interest his schoolmates. Hans was not like the other children, so they made fun of him.

3   Hans liked fairy tales and he liked puppet shows. He wrote some fairy tales of his own. He put on shows for his parents. But when Hans was only eleven, his father died. Now Hans had to leave school and go to work. He wanted to be a singer or an actor. He liked ballet, too. But he did not find steady work.

4   Hans continued to write his plays and stories. He wanted to sell them, but no one wanted to buy them. One day, a man read one of Hans's plays. He liked it and wanted to help Hans. He made it possible for Hans go back to school.

5   Hans wrote many things, but people know his fairy tales best. "The Emperor's New Clothes" tells about an emperor who is tricked into buying some fancy cloth. He cannot see any cloth, but the men who sell the cloth lie to him. They say that people who cannot see it are dull, so the emperor pretends to see it. He does not want them to think he is dull. He pays the men and they pretend to make fine clothes for him. When the clothes are done, the emperor goes out among his people. The people think that there

is something wrong with them, because they do not see the fine clothes. So they pretend that they do. But then a little boy cries, "Look! The emperor has no clothes!" Everyone sees that this is true. Now the emperor knows that the cloth was not real after all. He is naked!

6   Many of Hans's fairy tales have a lesson. What was the lesson for the emperor? He should not have listened to people who wanted to fool him. He should have believed his own eyes!

7   Hans's life was like his story of the ugly duckling that grew up to be a swan. When Hans was young, people made fun of him. But when he grew up, people loved his stories. And they loved him.

Modeled Instruction

Directions: Below is an example of a question that can be answered by drawing conclusions about the passage. Follow the strategy that is explained to help choose the correct answer.

---

1 Why do you think Hans liked fairy tales?

- Ⓐ because they were short

- Ⓑ because they were fun to read

- Ⓒ because he learned lessons from them

- Ⓓ because his teacher read them to him

Strategy: Look for details in the passage that help you to draw conclusions. Think about what these details tell you. Ask yourself what you can conclude from the facts you are given.

Use this strategy to decide which answer is correct.

 Ⓐ because they were short

Hans loved to read and he loved fairy tales. He probably would not mind if a fairy tale was short or long. Nothing in the passage tells you that fairy tales are all short. From this you can conclude that *choice "A" cannot be correct.*

 Ⓑ because they were fun to read

You know that Hans's life was difficult. So it would make sense for him to want to do something he enjoyed. Reading fairy tales was probably fun for Hans. From this you can conclude that *choice "B" must be the correct answer.*

 Ⓒ because he learned lessons from them

The passage does say that many fairy tales teach a lesson. But Hans probably would not want to be taught a lesson whenever he read a fairy tale. You can conclude that *choice "C" cannot be correct.*

 Ⓓ because his teacher read them to him

The passage tells you that Hans had to leave school. The passage does not talk about his teachers at all. From this you can conclude that *choice "D" cannot be correct.*

Guided Instruction

Directions: Use the hints to answer the questions below. For question 2, you must choose the correct answer. For question 3, you will need to write out your answer.

2 **You can conclude that Hans was a bright boy because—**

(A) he helped his father make shoes

(B) he did not go to school very often

(C) his family did not have much money

(D) he wrote his own fairy tales and put on plays

Hint: Find details in the passage that tell about Hans's childhood. Ask yourself what you can conclude from this information.

3 **Why do you think Hans had to go to work after his father died?**

_____

_____

_____

_____

_____

_____

_____

_____

_____

_____

Hint: Think about what the passage says about Hans's family. What would Hans get from a job? Think about what you can conclude from this information.

Independent Study

Directions: Answer the following questions on your own. For questions 4, 5, and 6, choose the correct answer. For question 7, you must write out your answer.

4 **From the passage it can be concluded that—**

  Ⓐ Hans looked like an ugly duckling

  Ⓑ "The Emperor's New Clothes" was a true story

  Ⓒ Hans's favorite fairy tale was "The Emperor's New Clothes"

  Ⓓ people loved reading about the duckling that became a swan

5 **Why was the man who liked Hans's play so important to Hans?**

  Ⓐ He became Hans's best friend.

  Ⓑ He told Hans what to write in his fairy tales.

  Ⓒ He gave Hans a chance to learn more, so he could write better.

  Ⓓ He gave Hans money so that his family would not be poor anymore.

6 **Why do you think people loved Hans Christian Andersen?**

  Ⓐ He wrote fairy tales about them.

  Ⓑ They loved the stories that he wrote.

  Ⓒ He taught them how to write fairy tales.

  Ⓓ When he became rich, he gave them money.

7 **What can you conclude about the kind of person Hans Christian Andersen was?**

_____

_____

_____

_____

_____

_____

_____

Skill 11: Make Inferences

An inference is what is most likely to be true. It is an opinion based on information in the passage. Information may include maps, charts, pictures, and photos. Inferences are not always correct.

INFORMATION	*Ann is ill.*
INFERENCE	*She will not go to school tomorrow.*

Directions: Read the passage below. Look at the chart. The passage and chart are followed by questions that can be answered by making inferences. Use this information to answer all of the questions on pages 57–59.

GROWING AND CHANGING

1   When you were born, you looked like a person. In many ways, you looked a lot like you do now. You had arms and legs. You had eyes and ears, a nose and a mouth. Now you are bigger. But your body is still much the same as when you were born.

2   Many baby animals do not look like their parents at all. And they change a few times while they grow. A butterfly starts out as an egg. Then a caterpillar comes out of the egg. It does not look like a butterfly! Not yet.

Photo: ©Norma Prause-Brewer

3   Look at the pictures on this page. They show the different stages of a butterfly's life. It starts as an egg. Follow the arrows to see how the egg becomes a butterfly.

4   A butterfly lays its egg on a leaf. When the caterpillar comes out of the egg, it eats the leaf. It eats all the time, and it grows very fast. As it grows, the caterpillar sheds its skin a few times. Then the caterpillar turns into a pupa. The pupa looks like a small sack. Inside the pupa, the caterpillar changes and takes a new shape. Finally, a butterfly comes out of the pupa. Its wings are wet and folded. When the wings are dry, the butterfly can fly. At last, it looks like the beautiful insect we know.

5   A lot of other baby bugs do not look like their parents at first. But most of them do not change as much as a butterfly does. An ant starts out as a larva that looks like a worm. Then it changes to a pupa. The pupa turns into an ant.

6   A baby cricket is more like you. It looks just like its parents as soon as it comes out of its egg. All it needs is its wings. It will shed its skin many times as it grows. But it does not change the way it looks.

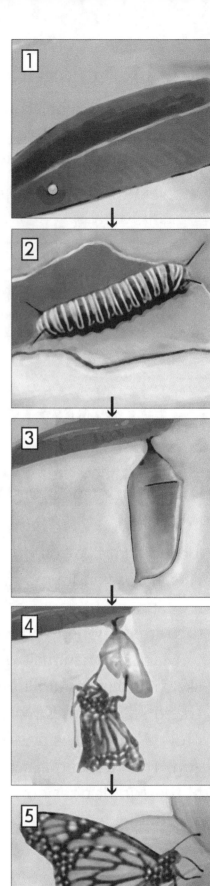

Modeled Instruction

Directions: Below is an example of a question that can be answered by making inferences about the passage. Follow the strategy that is explained to help choose the correct answer.

> **1 If a butterfly cannot dry its wings—**
>
> Ⓐ it will fly slowly
>
> Ⓑ it will not be able to fly
>
> Ⓒ it will not become a pupa
>
> Ⓓ other butterflies will fly away from it

Strategy: Think about what the details in the passage suggest. You will not be able to find specific facts that tell you the answer. You must look at each answer choice and try to find details to support it. Ask yourself which answer makes the most sense.

Use this strategy to decide which answer is correct.

 Ⓐ it will fly slowly

The details tell you that the butterfly's wings need to dry. They tell you that when the wings are dry, then the butterfly can fly. It does not seem as if the butterfly could fly at all if its wings are wet. Therefore, *choice "A" cannot be correct.*

 Ⓒ it will not become a pupa

The details in the passage tell you that a caterpillar becomes a pupa. The butterfly comes from the pupa. A butterfly does not ever become a pupa. Therefore, *choice "C" cannot be correct.*

 Ⓑ it will not be able to fly

The details seem to say that the butterfly must have dry wings in order to fly. Therefore, *choice "B" would be the best answer to this question.*

 Ⓓ other butterflies will fly away from it

There are no details about how butterflies act together. There is no information about this at all. Therefore, *choice "D" cannot be correct.*

Guided Instruction

Directions: Use the hints to answer the questions below. For question 2, you must choose the correct answer. For question 3, you will need to write out your answer.

2 Which of these probably best tells how a moth grows?

(A) It looks just like its parents when it is born.

(B) It grows in a way that is like the butterfly.

(C) It looks like a cricket at first.

(D) It grows like an ant does.

Hint: Think about how a moth looks. Is a moth like a butterfly? Is a moth like a cricket or an ant? What can you infer from this information?

3 The author says that a cricket is "more like you." What does this mean?

_____

_____

_____

_____

_____

_____

_____

_____

_____

_____

_____

Hint: Think about what the details in the passage tell you. Are they saying that you look more like a cricket than a butterfly? Are they saying that you are just like a cricket? Is there some way that you are like a cricket?

Independent Study

Directions: Answer the following questions on your own. For questions 4, 5, and 6, choose the correct answer. For question 7, you must write out your answer.

4 From the pictures you can tell that—

Ⓐ a butterfly becomes an egg

Ⓑ a caterpillar comes out of a pupa

Ⓒ a caterpillar is an egg and then a pupa

Ⓓ a butterfly comes out of an egg on a leaf

5 When an ant comes out of its pupa, it most likely—

Ⓐ begins working in the ant colony

Ⓑ becomes an egg again

Ⓒ looks for its mother

Ⓓ turns into a caterpillar

6 What do you think would happen if a butterfly pupa were opened before it was ready?

Ⓐ The butterfly would come out sooner.

Ⓑ The butterfly would begin as an egg again.

Ⓒ The butterfly or caterpillar inside would die.

Ⓓ The caterpillar would make a new pupa.

7 Why do you think the butterfly's wings are folded when it is inside the pupa?

_____

_____

_____

_____

_____

_____

_____

Skill 12: Point of View and Purpose

Every author has a point of view and a purpose.

POINT OF VIEW This is what an author believes about something.
PURPOSE   This is the reason why the author wrote the passage.

Directions: Read the letter below. It is followed by questions that can be answered by telling the author's point of view and purpose. Use this letter to answer all the questions on pages 62–64.

A Gift from the Heart

1   Did you ever make a present for a friend? Have you made a card for your mom or dad? Sometimes there are things in stores that you would like to buy as gifts, but you don't have enough money. Then you should make something. It will be a great gift. It will show how much you care.

2   Your gift can be a simple card that you can make in a few minutes. Or it can be something that requires a great deal of time and effort. But first you do some thinking. You consider what the person would like. Maybe you will choose to make something that is the person's favorite color. You decide what you will use to make the present. It could be made out of clay. It might be made of wood or paper. It could be yarn or rocks and twigs. That is a lot of thinking about something! Finally, you make your choice and begin.

3   I remember a birthday I once had. I got some music I liked. I got a soft, warm pair of red slippers. I got a beautiful ring. And my little sister's present was a picture that she had drawn of the two of us.

4   My music was wonderful and I listened to it a lot. I loved my cozy red slippers. I wore them until they had holes in them! I loved to look at the

pretty new ring on my finger. But what do you think was the best gift of all? What did I want to show to everyone? It was my little sister's picture, because I knew that Ellie had thought a lot about what she would draw. She drew me in my favorite shirt. We were eating ice cream. I had my favorite flavor—chocolate chip! There were flowers all around us. And there were birds in the air. A bright yellow sun was shining in the sky. We looked so happy. And every time I look at Ellie's drawing I feel that happy again.

5   I enjoyed my other gifts. I liked them very much! But there is something very special about my little sister's picture. That is why it still hangs by my desk. Ellie thinks it is funny that I still have it. She is older now, and wants to make me a new picture. She says it will be better. I tell her to go ahead, and I will hang that one, too. But I won't take down the old one. It was a gift from her heart.

Modeled Instruction

Directions: Below is an example of a question that can be answered by analyzing the author's point of view and purpose. Follow the strategy that is explained to help choose the correct answer.

---

1 The author of this passage probably believes that—

Ⓐ you should not buy presents

Ⓑ anyone can make some kind of gift

Ⓒ you should always buy cards

Ⓓ people should always draw pictures about ice cream

Strategy: Think about the entire passage, not just a section of it. In order to understand an author's point of view or purpose, you must consider all of the information that is given. If you only focus on a few details, you may get the wrong idea about what the author believes or is trying to say.

Use this strategy to decide which answer is correct.

 Ⓐ **you should not buy presents**

The author talks about how nice it is to make a gift. But the author also says that there may be things in the store that you would like to buy. Therefore, *choice "A" cannot be correct.*

 Ⓒ **you should always buy cards**

The author says that a simple card is something that can be made. So you don't have to buy one. Therefore, *choice "C" cannot be correct.*

 Ⓑ **anyone can make some kind of gift**

The author talks about many different kinds of gifts. It sounds as if a gift can be made of anything and can be very simple. It seems that the author feels that anyone can make something. Therefore, *choice "B" is the correct answer.*

 Ⓓ **people should always draw pictures about ice cream**

The picture that the author's sister drew shows them eating ice cream. But that is just one part of the picture. It is not why the author likes the picture so much. Therefore, *choice "D" cannot be correct.*

Guided Instruction

Directions: Use the hints to answer the questions below. For question 2, you must choose the correct answer. For question 3, you will need to write out your answer.

---

2 **The author of this story most likely agrees that—**

(A) store-bought presents are not useful

(B) it is hard to find something people really want in a store

(C) a handmade gift will always be welcome

(D) you should only give gifts that you make yourself

Hint: Consider each answer choice. Look for details in the essay to support each possible answer. Which choice is **best** supported by the details you can find?

---

3 **What are some things that you might think about when you make a gift?**

_____

_____

_____

_____

_____

_____

_____

_____

_____

_____

Hint: Think about things from the author's point of view. What does the author say about gifts? What does the story say about how people decide what to make?

Independent Study

Directions: Answer the following questions on your own. For questions 4, 5, and 6, choose the correct answer. For question 7, you must write out your answer.

4 **The author's main purpose for writing this story is to—**

(A) tell people that it is nice to make a present for someone

(B) get people to stop buying birthday gifts at stores

(C) tell people how to make a birthday card

(D) get people to draw more pictures

5 **The author would NOT agree that—**

(A) a lot of thought goes into a handmade gift

(B) most people will like getting a handmade gift

(C) it is possible to make gifts out of almost anything

(D) anything you see in a store, you can make at home

6 **Which of the following does the author believe to be true?**

(A) You do not need money to give a nice gift.

(B) People who can't draw should not try to make anything.

(C) It is better to get no present than to get one from a store.

(D) Everyone should have a picture just like the one Ellie drew.

7 **Why does the author believe that handmade gifts can be more special than store-bought gifts?**

_____

_____

_____

_____

_____

_____

_____

_____

_____

Skill 13: Literary Forms and Sources of Information

There are different forms of writing. For example, a poem is different from a story. There are different sources of information. For example, information about current events is found in a newspaper.

Directions: The passage is followed by questions that can be answered by being able to tell one type of writing from another and by knowing where to find different kinds of writing. Use this passage to answer all of the questions on pages 67–69.

Paul Bunyan

1   Have you heard of Paul Bunyan? There are many stories about him and his friend, Babe. Paul was a logger who cut down trees and Babe was his blue ox. The stories tell of amazing things that are very hard to believe. That is because Paul and Babe are not real. They were made up by loggers who told stories as they sat around campfires at night. The stories spread from one logging camp to another. Here are some of the tales.

2   Paul was such a huge baby that it took five giant storks to bring him to his parents. After only one week, he was as big as his father! He grew up to be about 64 ax handles tall.

3   During the Winter of the Blue Snow, Paul saved Babe from drowning. Babe grew to be a very large ox that could eat thirty large bundles of hay for a snack! It would take a crow a whole day to fly from one of Babe's horns to the other.

4   Paul's world was filled with people and animals that were larger than life. He worked with seven men who were all over six feet tall—sitting down! Paul's cook made huge meals. His soup kettle was very large. He had to row a boat out into the soup and shovel in the vegetables. The pancakes he made were so big that they were hard to flip. The cook's son added popcorn to the batter. Then the pancakes flipped themselves!

PART A: The 14 Essential Skills for Reading Success — One-by-One

5   Paul's purple cow named Lucy gave a lot of milk. One winter it got so cold that Lucy's milk turned to ice cream before it got to the pail! Paul even had huge insects. He trained giant ants to help with the logs. Each ant was the size of an elephant!

6   Paul Bunyan was so very big,

7   He made trees look like tiny twigs.

8   With just one step he walked a mile,

9   And Babe was with him all the while.

10   There are many stories of Babe and Paul,

11   But you'd be silly to believe them all!

12   The tales are so tall, they cannot be true,

13   But I wish I'd met Paul and Babe, don't you?

Paul Bunyan monument, Bemidji, Minnesota, 1939.
Photographer: John Vachon, 1914-1975.
Courtesy of Library of Congress.

Modeled Instruction

Directions: Below is an example of a question that can be answered by identifying literary forms and sources of information. Follow the strategy that is explained to help choose the correct answer.

---

1 The stories about Paul Bunyan and Babe in this passage are examples of—

(A) tall tales

(B) biographies

(C) fairy tales

(D) realistic stories

Strategy: Think about the following:

- What can you tell about the style in which the passage was written?
- What type of information can be found in the passage?
- Why might you choose to read the passage?

Asking yourself these three questions will help you to choose the correct answer.

Use this strategy to decide which answer is correct.

 (A) **tall tales**

In tall tales, people are often much larger or stronger than ordinary people. They can do things that ordinary people cannot do. A tall tale is not a true story. It is about things that could not happen. Based on this information, *choice "A" is correct.*

 (C) **fairy tales**

A fairy tale is about fairies, witches, giants, and others that are not real. The things that happen are not real. The stories in this passage are unbelievable, but there really are loggers and oxen. Since this choice does NOT describe the passage, *choice "C" is not the best answer.*

 (B) **biographies**

A biography is a story about the life of a real person. These stories are not about a real person. Therefore, *choice "B" cannot be the answer.*

 (D) **realistic stories**

Realistic stories tell about things that could be true and could really happen. Since this does NOT describe the passage, *choice "D" cannot be the answer.*

Guided Instruction

Directions: Use the hints to answer the questions below. For question 2, you must choose the correct answer. For question 3, you will need to write out your answer.

2 The purpose of this passage is to—

Ⓐ teach a lesson

Ⓑ tell how to do something

Ⓒ entertain you

Ⓓ get you to do something

Hint: Describe the passage to yourself. Think about why the passage was probably written. Why might someone choose to read this passage?

3 Explain how you can tell that this passage is NOT an example of a news story.

_____

_____

_____

_____

_____

_____

_____

_____

_____

_____

_____

_____

Hint: A news story tells about real events. Its purpose is to tell people what is happening in the world around them. Think about how this compares to the passage you read.

Independent Study

Directions: Answer the following questions on your own. For questions 4, 5, and 6, choose the correct answer. For question 7, you must write out your answer.

4 If you want to read more stories about Paul and Babe, you might look in—

Ⓐ a dictionary

Ⓑ a book of magic

Ⓒ a cookbook

Ⓓ a story book

5 What kind of writing is at the end of this passage?

Ⓐ a play

Ⓑ a poem

Ⓒ a news story

Ⓓ a fairy tale

6 How would this story be different if it were a play?

Ⓐ It would be very short.

Ⓑ It would have more characters.

Ⓒ It would tell a story about real people and real events.

Ⓓ It would show what each person in the play should say.

7 What makes the end of this passage different from the rest of the passage? How can you tell that it is a different kind of writing?

_____

_____

_____

_____

_____

_____

_____

_____

Skill 14: Prior Knowledge

This is information that you know before you read the passage.

Directions: Read the passage below. The passage is followed by questions that can be answered by using what you already know. Use this passage to answer all of the questions on pages 72–74.

A Walk in the Woods

1   Mike was excited about today's field trip. Mr. Ying was taking the class into the hills outside the city. They would walk on the trails and see the tall trees.

2   The class was going to talk about the changing color of the leaves. Mike's favorite leaves had many colors. Some were red and yellow with green edges. Others were yellow, orange, and green.

3   One time Mike had picked up colorful leaves on his way home from school. His Uncle Ed had helped him press them. First, Mike placed the leaves on a piece of waxed paper. Then he put another piece of the paper on top of the leaves. Ed covered the waxed paper with a towel. He moved a hot iron around on the towel. Then Ed put the iron aside and removed the towel. Mike held his pressed leaves up to the window. They looked very pretty, so he taped them up there. He wanted to collect more leaves today. His mother had promised to help him press them.

4   The class took a school bus to the hills in the state park. It was a perfect day for looking at colors. The sun was bright in a deep blue sky.

5   As Mike and his friends walked along, Mr. Ying pointed out different trees. They saw maple, elm, birch, and oak trees. He explained that there are two types of trees.

6   "All the trees that we are seeing today drop their leaves during this season," said Mr. Ying. "But some trees have needles instead of leaves. They keep their needles all year. That is why they are called evergreens. Pine trees and fir trees are evergreens."

7   "It's good that we came today," added Mr. Ying. "Next week might be too late."

8   At the top of the hill, the class had a wonderful view of the valley below. The trees spread out before them like a colorful carpet. Mike took a picture with his camera. One of his friends said, "Take another one! I didn't bring my camera." So Mike took a lot of pictures of the beautiful trees. He also took some pictures of his friends. Then he took a picture of Mr. Ying, and that finished his roll of film.

9   After a picnic lunch, it was time to go. They gathered some leaves from the ground. Mike picked up acorns, too. He knew he would not be able to press them, but he would keep them on his shelf at home.

Modeled Instruction

Directions: Below is an example of a question that can be answered by applying prior knowledge. Follow the strategy that is explained to help choose the correct answer.

---

1 Why did Mike need his mother to help him press the leaves?

Ⓐ He could burn himself on the hot iron.

Ⓑ He would not know which leaves to press.

Ⓒ He could not remember how to do it.

Ⓓ He would not be able to find the waxed paper.

Strategy: First look for information in the passage that can be used to help answer the question. Then think about what you already know. What you already know should help you to better understand the information in the passage. Choose the answer that makes the most sense to you.

Use this strategy to decide which answer is correct.

 Ⓐ **He could burn himself on the iron.**

Mike's uncle used an iron to press the leaves. You already know that a hot iron can burn you. It would be best if Mike had an adult to help him with the iron. Therefore, *choice "A" is the best possible answer.*

 Ⓒ **He could not remember how to do it.**

The passage tells how Mike remembers what he and his Uncle Ed did. This tells you that Mike does remember how to do it. Therefore, *choice "C" cannot be the answer.*

 Ⓑ **He would not know which leaves to press.**

Mike chose the leaves that he and his Uncle Ed pressed. He would probably choose the leaves that he and his mother would press, too. Therefore, *choice "B" cannot be the answer.*

 Ⓓ **He would not be able to find the waxed paper.**

Mike could look for the waxed paper or ask his mother where it was. This would not mean he needed help pressing the leaves. Therefore, *choice "D" cannot be the answer.*

Guided Instruction

Directions: Use the hints to answer the questions below. For question 2, you must choose the correct answer. For question 3, you will need to write out your answer.

---

2 Mr. Ying must be—

   Ⓐ Mike's father

   Ⓑ Mike's teacher

   Ⓒ a scientist

   Ⓓ a park ranger

Hint: Think about what the passage says about who is going on the field trip. Think about what you already know about going to school.

---

3 Why did Mike think that he would not be able to press the acorns?

_____

_____

_____

_____

_____

_____

_____

_____

_____

_____

_____

Hint: You have seen an acorn or a picture of one. Think about what you know about an acorn. What would happen if Mike tried to iron an acorn?

Independent Study

Directions: Answer the following questions on your own. For questions 4, 5, and 6, choose the correct answer. For question 7, you must write out your answer.

4 What will NOT happen in the park in the next couple of weeks?

Ⓐ The leaves will turn brown.

Ⓑ The tree branches will be bare.

Ⓒ The leaves will become more colorful.

Ⓓ The leaves will fall from the trees.

5 Mike will probably—

Ⓐ take the film out of his camera, and take it to a store

Ⓑ give his camera away because it has run out of film

Ⓒ give his camera to his friend who did not bring one

Ⓓ take more pictures as they walk back down the hill

6 Which of these would be the best place to see colorful leaves?

Ⓐ a shopping mall

Ⓑ a city street

Ⓒ a snowy mountain

Ⓓ a country road

7 What time of year is it in this story? How can you tell? Explain the reasons for your answers.

_____

_____

_____

_____

_____

_____

_____

_____

_____

PART B

The 14 Essential Skills for Reading Success

All Together

Section 1: Modeled Instruction and Guided Instruction

Each of the fourteen reading comprehension skills are taught all together in this part. Part B is divided into two sections.

Section 1: Modeled Instruction and Guided Instruction

In this section, you will read a passage and answer fourteen questions. The questions will be both multiple-choice and open-ended. Each question covers one of the fourteen essential skills. There will be a *Reminder* to help you remember the strategy needed to answer each question.

Section 2: Independent Study

This section is made up of four different types of passages. All the passages are about one theme. Each passage has fourteen essential skill questions. You are on your own to answer them. At the end of the theme, there will be three questions about how the passages are connected to the theme.

Theme A: *Everybody Wants a Pet*

Section 1: Modeled Instruction and Guided Instruction

On the pages that follow are several passages. Each passage is followed by fourteen questions. You will use the skills that you practiced in Part A to answer them. There are reminders below each question to help you remember which skill you should use to answer it.

Directions: Read the passage below. Then answer the questions that follow. Use the reminders to help you remember the strategy for answering each type of question.

JOHNNY APPLESEED

1   Suppose there was someone named Betty Smith. She thought that everyone should know how to bake bread. She went from town to town teaching people how to bake. People started to call her Betty Bread.

2   Suppose there was someone named Will Carter. He thought that everyone should play checkers. He made checker sets. Then he went from town to town giving them away. People started to call him Will Checkers.

3   Suppose someone named John Chapman thought that everyone should have apple trees. He planted apple trees. He gave apple seeds to people who wanted to plant their own trees. Can you guess what people started to call him? That's right! He was called Johnny Appleseed.

4   There is no one who is called Betty Bread. There is no one named Will Checkers. But there really was a Johnny Appleseed. He was an interesting person.

5   Johnny Appleseed was born over two hundred years ago. He loved nature. And he loved apple trees. Their flowers are beautiful. And these

trees *provide* food. You can eat an apple. Or you can bake an apple pie. You can make applesauce.

6   Many people were moving west in those days. Johnny Appleseed left his home. He traveled west, too. Johnny walked alone. Often he slept outdoors.

7   For almost fifty years, Johnny helped people who were moving out west. He gave them apple seeds. Apple seeds are very small. They were easy for the travelers to carry.

8   Johnny moved from place to place. When he found a good spot, he would clear the land. Then he would plant his apple seeds in neat rows. Even today you can pick apples from some of these trees.

9   Johnny Appleseed helped people. Many called this kind and gentle man their friend. On his tombstone it says, "He lived for others."

10   Johnny Appleseed is still remembered today. There is a Johnny Appleseed School. There is a Johnny Appleseed Park. And every year there is a Johnny Appleseed Fair. In these ways, people continue to say "Thank you" to Johnny Appleseed.

Directions: Answer the following questions using the reminders provided to help you recall the correct strategy for answering each type of question.

Facts and Details

1 When was Johnny Appleseed born?

(A) five years ago

(B) about ten years ago

(C) one hundred weeks ago

(D) over two hundred years ago

Reminder: The answer to this question can be found right in the passage. Look for key words. Read the sentences with these key words very carefully to find the detail or fact needed to answer the question correctly.

Main Idea

2 This passage mainly tells about—

Ⓐ a woman named Betty Bread

Ⓑ how to grow apple trees

Ⓒ a man who planted apple trees

Ⓓ how people made applesauce

⁎ **Reminder:** The main idea is what the whole story is about. To answer this question correctly you need to think about the entire passage, not just one part.

Sequence

3 Which of these events happened first?

Ⓐ Johnny lived out west.

Ⓑ Johnny left his home.

Ⓒ A school was named after Johnny.

Ⓓ His tombstone said, "He lived for others."

⁎ **Reminder:** Find each of the answer choices within the passage. Make a timeline to help you choose the correct answer.

Language and Vocabulary

4 **The word** *provide* **in paragraph 5 means—**

(A) to eat

(B) to give

(C) to raise

(D) to plant

✳ Reminder: This type of question asks you to identify the meaning of a word. To find the meaning of a word you must think about how the word is used in the passage.

Character, Plot, and Setting

5 **Why does Johnny Appleseed's tombstone say, "He lived for others"?**

_____

_____

_____

_____

✳ Reminder: To answer this type of question you must think about a character in the passage. Consider the actions of the character and the events that take place.

_____

_____

_____

_____

_____

_____

_____

Cause and Effect

6 **When Johnny Appleseed found good land, he would clear it because—**

(A) he wanted to build a house

(B) he wanted people to like him

(C) he wanted to plant apple trees

(D) he wanted people to come and visit

Reminder: Cause and effect go together. To answer this type of question you must find the event or action in the answer choice that goes with the event or action in the question.

Compare and Contrast

7 **How are Johnny Appleseed and Will Checkers different?**

(A) Johnny Appleseed was a real person, but Will Checkers is not.

(B) Johnny Appleseed baked apple pies, but Will Checkers did not.

(C) Will Checkers liked to play games, but Johnny Appleseed did not.

(D) Will Checkers was friends with Betty Baker, but Johnny Appleseed was not.

Reminder: Compare questions ask you to tell how things are alike. Contrast questions ask you to tell how things are different. Use details from the passage to support your answer.

Facts and Opinions

8 Which of the following is NOT a fact?

(A) You can eat an apple.

(B) He was an interesting person.

(C) Johnny walked alone.

(D) Apple seeds are very small.

Predict Outcomes

9 How might things have been different if Johnny Appleseed had not gone west?

(A) There would be fewer apple trees in that part of the county.

(B) No one would have known about apple pies and applesauce.

(C) More people would have learned to bake bread.

(D) Apple seeds would have been much larger.

Reach Conclusions

10 **Why do you think Johnny Appleseed had so many friends?**

_____

_____

_____

_____

_____

_____

_____

_____

_____

_____

_____

_____

_____

_____

_____

Make Inferences

11 Since Johnny Appleseed walked everywhere—

Ⓐ his travels took longer than if he rode on a horse

Ⓑ he was able to meet many more people

Ⓒ he didn't have time to build a house

Ⓓ he could carry only a few apple seeds

Reminder: Facts and details in a passage can suggest an answer without actually stating the answer. These questions are asking you to decide what events or details mean.

Point of View and Purpose

12 The author of the passage probably believes that—

Ⓐ everyone should plant apple trees

Ⓑ apples are the best kind of food to eat

Ⓒ Johnny Appleseed wasted a lot of time

Ⓓ it is good to try to help others as Johnny did

Reminder: How the author feels about a topic is a point of view. Why the author wrote a passage is the purpose. Details in a passage often suggest a point of view or purpose.

Literary Forms and Sources of Information

13 What kind of story is this?

Ⓐ fiction

Ⓑ folktale

Ⓒ biography

Ⓓ nonfiction

Reminder: To answer this question you must think about the style or type of writing. Different books contain different types of stories.

Prior Knowledge

14 What do you need to make an apple pie?

Ⓐ an oven

Ⓑ an electric mixer

Ⓒ a very large apple tree

Ⓓ Johnny Appleseed's apples

Reminder: The answer to this question cannot be found in the passage alone. In addition to details from the passage, you must use your own knowledge to help answer the question.

PART B

The 14 Essential Skills for Reading Success

All Together

Section 2:
Independent Study

Theme

Everybody Wants a Pet

Part B | Section 2: Independent Study

This section is made up of four different types of passages. All the passages are about one theme. Each passage has fourteen essential skill questions. You are on your own to answer them. At the end of the theme, there will be three questions about how the passages are connected to the theme.

B
Section 2: Independent Study

There are four passages in this Section. All the passages have something to do with Everybody Wants a Pet.

Theme A: Everybody Wants a Pet

Selection 1 | Directions: Read the passage below
and answer the questions that follow.

POTBELLIED PIGS

1   Many people have dogs, cats, and fish. Some have birds. And some might even have a snake. But did you know that there are many people who have pigs in their house? This may seem like a strange idea at first, but these animals make great pets. They can be friendly and they love to play!

2   Potbellied pigs were bought to the United States from Asia in the 1980s. At first these pigs cost a great deal of money. They do not cost so much today. Now, many people can *afford* them.

3   These pigs are much smaller than other pigs. They are about 24 inches tall. That's about the size of a small dog. But potbellied pigs can weigh up to 100 pounds. That is a lot less than a hog that can weigh over 1,000 pounds. But it's much heavier than a small dog.

4   Potbellied pigs can eat many things. They are not fussy. They like to eat fruits and vegetables. You don't have to buy special food that is just for pigs. But, as with all animals, make sure they always have enough water to drink.

5   These animals can cause some problems. Some like to defend their space. If you get too close, they will snap at you. But, with time, they can get used to you. They can be trained to be nicer. Potbellied pigs also like to dig in the dirt. This can be a problem if a pig is near a garden. But that problem can be solved, too. Just give it a spot of its own to dig and the pig will soon learn to leave the garden alone.

6   Please don't get the idea that these pigs are too much trouble. They aren't. They are very smart and can learn almost anything. If you take good care of them, potbellied pigs can live to be about 15 years old. Some live as long as 20 years. Now that you've learned about these animals, how would you like one as a pet?

Directions: Answer the following questions on your own.

1 **How much can a full-grown potbellied pig weigh?**

Ⓐ 1,000 pounds

Ⓑ 24 pounds

Ⓒ 15 pounds

Ⓓ 100 pounds

2 **What is the main idea of the fourth paragraph?**

Ⓐ Make sure the pig has enough water to drink.

Ⓑ Potbellied pigs love vegetables.

Ⓒ Potbellied pigs eat many things.

Ⓓ You can buy special food for pigs.

3 What happened before 1980?

Ⓐ There were not many potbellied pigs in Asia.

Ⓑ Not many people had potbellied pigs as pets.

Ⓒ Potbellied pigs lived mostly in the United States.

Ⓓ Many people kept potbellied pigs in the house.

4 What does *afford* mean?

Ⓐ to train pigs as pets

Ⓑ to have enough money

Ⓒ you really like something

Ⓓ a pig costs too much

5 Which word best describes potbellied pigs?

Ⓐ mean

Ⓑ clever

Ⓒ lazy

Ⓓ shy

6 What happens if a potbellied pig feels that you are getting too close?

Ⓐ It will be very nice to you.

Ⓑ It will try to dig in the dirt.

Ⓒ It will try to bite you.

Ⓓ It will not have enough food.

7 Describe two ways potbellied pigs are like other pets.

_____

_____

_____

_____

_____

_____

_____

_____

_____

_____

_____

_____

8 Which of the following is NOT a fact?

Ⓐ They came from Asia.

Ⓑ They need water.

Ⓒ They dig in the dirt.

Ⓓ They make great pets.

9 If a potbellied pig is near a garden, it will probably want to—

Ⓐ eat the vegetables

Ⓑ dig in the dirt

Ⓒ sleep

Ⓓ run

10 Why do so many people have potbellied pigs as pets?

Ⓐ They can be very playful.

Ⓑ They eat many types of food.

Ⓒ They like to dig outside in the dirt.

Ⓓ They never snap at someone.

11 You tell from the passage that some people—

Ⓐ don't like pigs as pets

Ⓑ like to have pets that are different

Ⓒ don't have much money

Ⓓ want to have a large backyard

12 Why did the author write this passage?

Ⓐ because he doesn't like cats and dogs

Ⓑ to show that these animals are smart

Ⓒ to describe a different type of pet

Ⓓ because he wants to buy a pig

13 What kind of story is this?

Ⓐ fiction

Ⓑ biography

Ⓒ folktale

Ⓓ nonfiction

14 What could be some problems with having a potbellied pig?

Selection 2 | Directions: Read the passage below
and answer the questions that follow.

Tammy's New Friend

1   Tammy liked walking to school every day. She would think about her homework and her friends. She would daydream. It was pleasant, but not very exciting. But one day her walk was very exciting indeed.

2   On Tuesday, Tammy left her house early. As she was walking along, Tammy noticed something out of the corner of her eye. Something moved in the bushes. Tammy went over to take a closer look. It was a turtle. It was very cute! There was still a lot of time before school started, so Tammy decided to take the turtle home.

3   When she got home, Tammy put the turtle in a large jar and left it in her bedroom. She thought about the turtle as she hurried to school. That day seemed very, very long. Tammy couldn't wait to get home to look at the turtle. She was sure that it would make an *ideal* pet.

4   Tammy went into her bedroom and looked in the jar. The turtle seemed to be sleeping. Tammy took it out of the jar and the turtle started to wiggle its legs. She gently put him back in the jar and went to find her mother.

5   Her mother was in the living room. Tammy told her all about the turtle. She asked her mother if she could keep it for a pet. Her mother did not speak for a while. Tammy waited. Finally her mother said, "Tammy, I think the turtle will make a great pet. You need to find out how to take care of it." Tammy hugged her and went to the library. She found two books on turtles. The books were very helpful.

6   First, she learned that this kind of turtle might grow as large as 6 inches. That's a good size for a pet. If she took care of it, the turtle could live for more than 20 years. She read that turtles are very gentle and will not bite

people. Tammy wanted to find out what turtles ate, but she could not find this. She decided to go to the pet store.

7   At the pet store, Tammy told Mr. Jones about her turtle. "Can you please help me, Mr. Jones? I want to take good care of my turtle."

8   Mr. Jones wrote a list and told Tammy to show it to her mother. Tammy thanked him. On the way home, she read the list:

20-GALLON FISH TANK
5-POUND BAG OF ROCKS
BOX OF TURTLE FOOD
WATER HEATER

9   When Tammy's mother read the list, she said, " Well, it looks like we better go see Mr. Jones about those supplies." During the ride to the pet store, Tammy decided that "Tony" would be a good name for the turtle. But what if it wasn't a boy? Then Tammy smiled. She had plenty of time to find out—about 20 years.

Directions: Answer the following questions on your own.

1 The passage did NOT say that—

Ⓐ Tammy found a turtle in the woods

Ⓑ Mr. Jones gave Tammy a list

Ⓒ Tammy stayed home from school

Ⓓ Tammy went to the library

2 Another good title for this passage would be—

Ⓐ "Tammy's Wish"

Ⓑ "Mr. Jones's Store"

Ⓒ "A Very Nice Mother"

Ⓓ "A New Home for Tony"

3 What does Tammy do right after she speaks to her mother?

(A) She walks to school.

(B) She goes into her bedroom.

(C) She visits the library.

(D) She goes to the pet shop.

4 An *ideal* pet is one that—

(A) lives in a tank

(B) lives a long time

(C) does not try to bite you

(D) is perfect in every way

5 How does Tammy change by the end of the passage?

(A) She likes her mother a lot more.

(B) She is looking forward to school.

(C) She doesn't like turtles any more.

(D) She has learned a lot about turtles.

6 Tammy went to see Mr. Jones because—

(A) she liked visiting pet stores

(B) she didn't know what turtles eat

(C) she didn't want to go to the library

(D) she always enjoyed talking to him

7 What do Tammy and Mr. Jones have in common?

Ⓐ They both like animals.

Ⓑ They both like to go walking.

Ⓒ They both enjoy reading books.

Ⓓ They both live near the library.

8 Which statement is a fact?

Ⓐ The books were very helpful.

Ⓑ That's a good size for a pet.

Ⓒ Turtles can live for more than 20 years.

Ⓓ It was very cute!

9 When Tammy and her mother return from the pet store, what will Tammy probably do next?

_____

_____

_____

_____

_____

_____

_____

_____

_____

_____

_____

_____

_____

_____

10 **A lesson to be learned from the story is that—**

(A) it is a good idea to go for a walk

(B) turtles are the best pets

(C) you need to know how to take care of a pet

(D) pet supplies can cost a lot of money

11 **Explain how you can tell from the passage that Tammy knows how to talk nicely to other people.**

_____

_____

_____

_____

_____

_____

_____

_____

_____

_____

_____

_____

_____

_____

_____

_____

_____

_____

_____

12 The author would agree that—

Ⓐ Mr. Jones was not helpful

Ⓑ Tammy should find another pet

Ⓒ turtles are gentle animals

Ⓓ turtles eat a lot of food

13 You might expect to find this passage in a book titled—

Ⓐ *Pet Supplies*

Ⓑ *This is a Library*

Ⓒ *The Pet Shop*

Ⓓ *Pet Stories*

14 What will Tammy need to put in the tank?

Ⓐ some water

Ⓑ new plants

Ⓒ another turtle

Ⓓ a bright light

Selection 3 | Directions: Read the passage below
and answer the questions that follow.

Getting His Wish

1   Today was Tim's birthday. His parents had promised to get him a dog for his birthday. They told him he could pick out any dog he liked.

2   There was a pet shop in town. Tim walked by it on his way to school. He saw all kinds of cute puppies in the window. It would be a great place to go with his parents to pick out his birthday present.

3   Tim wanted to make sure his parents took him to that pet store. Tim went to the hall closet in his house. He took out the telephone book and opened to page 157. He left it on the kitchen table. He wanted his parents to see the ad for the pet store.

4   Tim's mother came into the kitchen and looked at the page. "This looks interesting, Tim. And I wanted to tell you about another pet store. I see it on the way home from work every day." She turned to page 155 in the telephone book. "I'll let you decide which you like best," she said.

THE PUP PALACE
- We have the best puppies in town.
- Choose your pet from over 200 puppies.
- More puppies arrive every day.

Store Hours
Monday to Saturday: 9:00 A.M. – 7:00 P.M.
Sunday: 10:00 A.M. – 5:00 P.M.

157

PLENTY OF PETS
- We have fish, birds, cats and dogs.
- All the pet supplies you'll ever need are right here.
- Our prices are the best!

Store Hours
Monday to Friday: 10:00 A.M. – 8:00 P.M.
Saturday: 10:00 A.M. – 6:00 P.M.
Sunday: 11:00 A.M. – 5:00 P.M.

155

5   Tim looked again at both pages. He tried to make up his mind. Both stores looked great.

6   "Mom, I'd like to go to The Pup Palace first. I think I have a better chance of finding the dog I want there. If that doesn't work out we can go to Plenty of Pets."

7   "I'm sure you'll *select* the best puppy," his mother said with a smile.

8   Tim couldn't believe his longtime wish was about to come true! By this afternoon he would have his own dog. This was going to be the best birthday ever.

Directions: Answer the following questions on your own.

1 When is The Pup Palace open on Sunday?

Ⓐ 11:00 A.M. – 5:00 P.M.

Ⓑ 9:00 A.M. – 7:00 P.M.

Ⓒ 10:00 A.M. – 6:00 P.M.

Ⓓ 10:00 A.M. – 5:00 P.M.

2 The main idea of this passage is that—

Ⓐ the Pup Palace is a pet store

Ⓑ Tim walks home from school every day

Ⓒ Tim will get to pick out a dog today

Ⓓ Plenty of Pets sells puppies

3 Which of these events happened first?

Ⓐ Tim looked at page 155.

Ⓑ Tim's mother came into the kitchen.

Ⓒ Tim's mother read The Pup Palace ad.

Ⓓ Tim opened the telephone book to page 157.

4 In this passage, the word *select* in paragraph 6 means—

Ⓐ love

Ⓑ sell

Ⓒ cuddle

Ⓓ choose

5 The story takes place in—

Ⓐ Tim's home

Ⓑ the pet store

Ⓒ town

Ⓓ school

6 Explain why Tim left the open telephone book on the kitchen table.

_____

_____

_____

_____

_____

_____

_____

_____

_____

_____

7 **According to the passage how are the two pet stores different?**

Ⓐ   Plenty of Pets sells dogs.

Ⓑ   The Pup Palace is open on Saturday.

Ⓒ   The Pup Palace sells only puppies.

Ⓓ   Plenty of Pets is in a different town.

8 **Which statement from the passage is an example of an opinion?**

Ⓐ   We have the best puppies in town.

Ⓑ   Choose your pet from over 200 puppies.

Ⓒ   We have fish, birds, cats, and dogs.

Ⓓ   He left it on the kitchen table.

9 **The next thing that will probably happen is—**

Ⓐ   Tim's mother won't let him get a puppy

Ⓑ   Tim and his mother will go to The Pup Palace

Ⓒ   Tim will decide to find another telephone book

Ⓓ   Tim and his mother will go to Plenty of Pets

10 **Why do you think that Tim's mother opened to a different page in the telephone book?**

_____

_____

_____

_____

_____

_____

_____

_____

_____

_____

_____

_____

_____

_____

_____

_____

_____

_____

_____

11 How can you tell from the passage that Tim's mother respects his opinions?

Ⓐ She knows that her choice is best.

Ⓑ She wants him to get another dog.

Ⓒ She lets him explain his reasons.

Ⓓ She will drive him to the pet store.

12 How did the author want you to feel when you read this story?

Ⓐ happy

Ⓑ tired

Ⓒ sad

Ⓓ angry

13 To find more about puppies you should look in—

Ⓐ a history book

Ⓑ an encyclopedia

Ⓒ a science book

Ⓓ a dictionary

14 When Tim brings the puppy home, what will he need?

Ⓐ a rug

Ⓑ a bottle

Ⓒ pet food

Ⓓ warm milk

The Letter

1   Ever since she was a small child, Anna loved animals. She fed the ducks in the park and went to the zoo many times. Now that she was getting older, Anna felt that she wanted her own pet. There was a problem. Anna's parents did not think she was old enough. Anna tried talking to them about it, but this didn't work. One night she sat down and wrote them a letter. She hoped this would make them change their minds.

2   Dear Mom and Dad,

3   I know you think I am too young, but I think it's time for me to have a pet of my own. I have thought about this a lot. I would like to explain the reasons I think this is a good idea.

4   Having a pet would be a good way for me to learn to take care of things. If I had a pet, I would have to learn to feed and clean it. This would be good practice for taking care of other things around the house. Both of you always say that you like it when I help out. This would help me learn to help even more.

5   If I had a pet, it might help me improve my schoolwork. First, I would spend less time watching television. I could also spend more time reading and learning about my pet. That means that I would read more books. My pet would also give me something to write about, so I would have better writing skills. This would really help my grades in school!

6   The pet would allow me to set a good example for Julie. She would also see me acting more like a grownup. I like teaching my little sister new things. I could show her how to take care of her own pet someday.

7   I hope you say yes.

8   Love, Anna

9   Anna knocked on her parents' door and went into their room. She handed her father the letter. She watched while her parents read it. Anna was so nervous. At last, her father put the letter down. Her parents smiled at each other and then at Anna.

10 "You know, Anna, it does seem as if you're old enough to get a pet," her mother said. "Let's talk about it at breakfast." It seemed as if Anna had made her point.

Directions: Answer the following questions on your own.

1 Anna did NOT—

  Ⓐ write a letter to her parents

  Ⓑ mail a letter to her parents

  Ⓒ like to go to the zoo

  Ⓓ try to help Julie

2 A good name for this story would be—

  Ⓐ "Anna Likes to Read Animal Stories"

  Ⓑ "Parents Can Change Their Minds"

  Ⓒ "Letters Are Fun to Write"

  Ⓓ "Children Need Pets"

3 According to the passage, when did Anna write the letter?

  Ⓐ after she changed her parents' minds

  Ⓑ before she fed the ducks in the park

  Ⓒ after the family had breakfast

  Ⓓ before she knocked on her parents' door

4 What does this sentence mean? "It seemed as if Anna had made her point."

  Ⓐ Anna had gotten her parents to agree with her.

  Ⓑ Anna was upset because her letter was long.

  Ⓒ Anna's parents enjoyed reading her letter.

  Ⓓ Her parents thought that Anna was wrong to want a pet.

5 Anna seems to be a smart person. Which clue supports this?

Ⓐ She hoped the letter would change her parents' minds.

Ⓑ She was very nervous as her parents read the letter.

Ⓒ She felt she was old enough to have a pet.

Ⓓ She explained her reasons for having a pet in her letter.

6 Anna wrote the letter because—

Ⓐ talking had not worked

Ⓑ she liked to write letters

Ⓒ she needed to practice writing

Ⓓ she wanted to visit the zoo again

7 According to the passage how are Anna and Julie alike?

Ⓐ They both have little sisters.

Ⓑ They both have the same parents.

Ⓒ They both watch too much television.

Ⓓ They both like to take care of things.

8 In the sentence "Anna felt that she wanted her own pet," which word signals that the sentence states an opinion?

Ⓐ pet

Ⓑ felt

Ⓒ own

Ⓓ wanted

9 **What do you think would have happened if Anna had not written the letter to her parents?**

_____

_____

_____

_____

_____

_____

_____

_____

_____

_____

_____

_____

_____

10 **What is a lesson that can be learned from the story?**

Ⓐ Having a pet is a great deal of trouble.

Ⓑ It's not a good idea to bother your parents.

Ⓒ You can try many ways to change people's minds.

Ⓓ You might not be old enough to have a pet of your own.

11 **How can a pet help Anna with her schoolwork?**

Ⓐ Anna will take care of the classroom pets.

Ⓑ Anna will tell her parents about other pets.

Ⓒ Anna will go to bed early and get up early.

Ⓓ Anna will spend more time reading and writing.

12 The author would agree that you should—

(A) never give up

(B) stay away from pets

(C) mind your own business

(D) do whatever you want to do

13 A book with more passages like this one could be called—

(A) *Improve Your Writing Skills*

(B) *All About Pets for Children*

(C) *How to Do Better Work at School*

(D) *How to Get Others to Agree with You*

14 If Anna gets the pet, what will she have to do before she goes to school in the morning?

_____

_____

_____

_____

_____

_____

_____

Theme Questions

Directions: The theme of Section 2 was "Everybody Wants a Pet." Answer these questions. They are about the four theme selections you just read.

1 How are Tim and Anna alike?

_____

_____

_____

_____

_____

_____

_____

_____

_____

_____

_____

_____

_____

_____

_____

_____

_____

2 Why might Tammy like to have a potbellied pig?

Ⓐ Potbellied pigs like turtles.

Ⓑ She likes taking care of pets.

Ⓒ She used to have a potbellied pig as a pet.

Ⓓ Her house has enough room for pigs and turtles.

3 How do the four selections help show that "Everybody Wants a Pet?"

_____

_____

_____

_____

_____

_____

_____

_____

_____

_____

_____

_____

_____

_____

_____

_____

_____

Notes